GERIATRIC DOG HEALTH & CARE
JOURNAL

A Complete Toolkit for the
GERIATRIC DOG CAREGIVER

DR. MARY GARDNER

ISBN: 978-1-956343-04-5

Ed: 1

Researcher and editor: Dr. Theresa Entriken

Interior design by: Ljiljana Pavkov
Illustrations by: Dusan Pavlic
Book cover design by: Victoria Black

Disclaimer

This book is not intended as a medical textbook. Every pet should receive an examination by their veterinarian prior to starting any treatment. Seek your veterinarian's advice if you have any concerns with your pet.

I do love cats! So please don't take offense that this book is focused on dogs.

Publisher: Rolled Toe Publishing (Books@GreyMuzzleVet.com)

   /drmarygardner 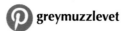 greymuzzlevet

Introduction

Your dog is wholly loved and well cared for, has the certainty and comfort of home, and probably experiences new or familiar adventures with you regularly. This good life can seem never ending! Then your dog may begin to exhibit out-of-character struggles that signal the ravages of Father Time. Your dog may have occasional urine accidents in the house. Rousing games of chase grow shorter and trigger stiffness. An easy stroll down the sidewalk induces fatigue, or getting up the stairs leads to a stumble. Favorite treats spark less interest. Barks sound harsher. The list can seem endless. As our dogs age, subtle developments take hold, and without our careful attention, seemingly drastic overnight changes can occur.

As a devoted pet parent, you know your dog's attitude, activities, and behavior best. It's crucial to track these things in a pet health journal such as this one, or on a calendar, or in your phone, or using an app—whichever method works best for you. When changes or symptoms arise, mention them and any concerns you have to your veterinary team—throughout your dog's life, but especially as your dog traverses his or her elder years. Some changes or symptoms (such as drinking more water, diarrhea, restlessness at night) may signal serious health issues, and other changes (such as more energy, less itchiness, better appetite) may signify health improvements. Keeping a pet health journal also helps you identify factors that may have contributed to the undesirable or desirable changes or symptoms you note. Jotting down events—such as when you feed a new diet, switch treats, visit a different dog park, start or finish a medication, host unfamiliar visitors, board your dog, place yoga mats across

Journal Templates

a slippery floor, or have your dog's pearly whites professionally polished—can provide clues that point to a cause or resolution of an ailment, illustrate patterns that signify trends, map recurring problems, and head off a serious health condition.

This journal is a companion to my book "It's Never Long Enough — A Practical Guide to Caring for Your Geriatric Dog." Together these resources provide a wealth of information and support as you care for your aging dog. The journal pages, questionnaires, logs, lists, assessments, and other templates I provide here will help you document and keep important information handy and organized. Use them all, or select those most relevant to you and your dog. This journal can also make partnering with your veterinarian easier as you continue to provide your pooch's best care! If you need more of these pages, you can find many of them on a special webpage I built. Use this QR code to access them.

I hope the tools contained in this journal allow you to better assess and manage your geriatric dog's health, feel empowered to make the best decisions, and continue enjoying your time with your grey muzzle family member.

Table of Contents

GERIATRIC DOG
HEALTH & CARE
JOURNAL

1

My dog's care team

S tart by jotting down your dog's key details along with a handy list of all those who help care for your dog.

My dog's name:
....

Date of birth: .... Adoption date: ....

Breed: .... Sex: .... Spayed or Neutered (Yes/No) ....

Veterinary Clinic Name and Address:
....

Veterinary Clinic Phone Number:
....

Primary Care Veterinarian:
....

Emergency Veterinary Hospital Name, Address, Phone:
....
....

Boarding Facility Information:
....

Doggie Daycare Information:
....

Groomer Information:
....

Dog Sitter Information:
....

Dog Walker Information:
....

Pet Insurance Information:
....

Microchip Information:
....

Emergency Caretaker Contact Information:
....

Other Important Contacts:
....
....

2

Health journal

Have you ever visited your doctor for an annual examination but then afterward mentally kicked yourself because you forgot to ask about a potential new health concern you noticed over the last couple months? Or maybe your doctor asked whether you'd been experiencing something that you hadn't considered a problem, but that turned out to be an early sign of a bigger issue? Similar situations often happen when pet parents visit their veterinarian. During veterinary visits or in times of illness, it can be hard for you to remember the nuances about changes you've noticed in your dog. So it's helpful to keep a health journal for your senior or geriatric dog. A journal will help you think about and recognize changes in your dog that may otherwise go unnoticed. Use the blank journal pages I've provided here, or create your own.

Write your observations about the types of normal and abnormal behaviors, changes, and symptoms your dog shows. Your entries may include all the details or serve as quick, general notes that support your recall abilities. To help, I've created a list of "Geriatric Dog Health Observations" questions for you to noodle on as you begin to journal about your dog's health. If your responses indicate changes in your dog, bring them up with your veterinarian. Review the question list every four to six months, to help you keep closer tabs on whether changes signal worsening trends that might otherwise catch you unaware.

In addition, take photos and videos six month intervals, and date each one you and your veterinarian monitor cha in your dog's appearance and behavi Beyond the health observations ques tions and blank journal pages, I've provided supplemental tools to help while you care for your geriatric dog, including forms to track your dog's specific symptoms, diagnostic tests and findings, diagnoses, treatments schedule changes, and more.

Geriatric Dog Health Observations

Eating/drinking

- What are your dog's favorite foods and treats? *(Record on the Nutrition and Treat Log on page 19)*

....

- Has your dog's food preferences changed in the last year?

....

- Has your dog's appetite decreased or increased?

....

- Are special enticements or is other assistance needed to get your dog to eat?

....

- Does your dog drop food while eating or have trouble chewing or swallowing?

....

- Does your dog have an increased thirst?

....

- Any vomiting?

....

Weight

- What is your dog's current weight?

....

- Has your dog lost weight without being on a diet or without getting extra exercise?

....

- Has your dog been gaining weight?

....

Sleep

- Where does your dog prefer to sleep?

....

- How many hours does your dog sleep during an average day?

....

- Does your dog sleep peacefully?

....

- What does your dog do if they get up during the night?

....

- Does your dog sleep more during the day than they used to and less at night?

....

Activity level

- What are your dog's favorite activities, toys, and games?

....

- Who are your dog's favorite people?

....

- Who are your dog's least favorite beings (squirrels, delivery people, neighbor dogs)?

....

- Does your dog have other favorite animal friends or playmates?

....

- Has your dog's activity decreased?

....

- If so, over what time period—the last few days, weeks, or months, or during the last year?

....

Strength and vitality

- Has your dog's energy decreased in the last year?

....

- Does your dog seem less interested in exercise or favorite activities?

....

- Is your dog weaker during exercise or less tolerant of exercise?

....

Mobility

- Does your dog need help on stairs?

....

- Does your dog have trouble getting into or out of the car?

....

- Any difficulty jumping on or off the bed or couch?

....

- Need help getting up from lying down?

....

- Does your dog drag their feet or toes?

....

- Has your dog's gait changed (walks slower or limps)?

....

Urine, feces, and house training

- Have you noticed an increase or decrease in urination?

....

- Any urinary or fecal accidents indoors?

....

- Does your dog have urine leakage while resting?

....

• Has the appearance or consistency of your dog's feces changed? Any diarrhea? Constipation?

....

• Does your dog pass a fecal ball during a walk without seeming to notice?

....

Ears, eyes, nose, mouth, throat, and breathing

• Have you noticed a change in your dog's hearing?

....

• Is your dog more or less reactive to noises?

....

• Does your dog have vision problems in bright light? In dim light? At night? Up close?

....

• A runny nose or sneezing?

....

• Watery or gooey discharge around the eyes?

....

• Bad breath?

....

• Does your dog's bark sound different?

....

• Does your dog repeatedly clear their throat?

....

• Does your dog pant more frequently?

....

• Does your dog breathe faster or heavier?

....

• Any coughing?

....

Skin, coat, and toenails

- Does your dog have increased or excessive itching?

....

- Lumps or bumps on or under the skin?

....

- Does your dog have unpleasant or odd skin or ear odor?

....

- Does your dog frequently lick or chew their skin or hair?

....

- Is your dog's skin or fur flaky, dry, or oily?

....

- Have you noticed longer toenails?

....

- Does your dog enjoy baths? Being brushed or combed?

....

- Is your dog's coat thinning? Dull?

....

- Does your dog have areas of hair loss?

....

Temperature and overall comfort

- Does your dog seek out new or unusual areas to rest that are warm, cold, soft, sunny, or hard?

....

- Does your dog shiver easily?

....

- Does your dog pant excessively?

....

Mentation

(If your dog exhibits these signs, see also the "Cognitive Assessment and Health Concerns for Dogs" form)

- Is your dog less excited to greet you when you get home?

....

- Has your dog been less interactive with the family?

....

- More clingy or anxious?

....

- Does your dog pace during the day or night?

....

- Stare off into space?

....

- Seem irritable or act more aggressively?

....

- Do they seem disoriented or distant?

....

- Become agitated at certain times of the day?

....

- Get stuck in odd locations or appear lost?

....

- Vocalize inappropriately (bark at night for no apparent reason)?

....

- Do they circle? (If so, is it one direction or both?)

....

- Have they had a seizure?

....

NOTES

3

Meals and treats

Nutrition is an integral component of your dog's wellness, and diet is a key factor in helping prevent or manage many different ailments. So an important component of your dog's veterinary visits includes discussing your dog's diet, appetite, caloric intake, and activity levels. As part of your pet's nutritional assessment, your veterinarian may ask you to provide a diet history for your dog.

An accurate diet history can be difficult to recall during the veterinary visit, so use the form I've created here and update it as needed, for example if you need to switch to a different diet or add a new treat. Or at the very least, take a picture of your pet's food and treats in their original packaging so the information is easily readable for you to share with your veterinarian.

Nutrition and Treat Log:

Daily diet (brand and name, type [kibble, canned, fresh, frozen], flavor, or home cooked diet recipe [with all ingredients and amounts]): ....

....

Amount fed per meal (cups or ounces): ....

Mealtime frequency: ....

Daily treats (brand and name, type, flavor): ....

Table foods my dog receives, amounts, and frequency fed: ....

....

Date new diet was introduced (and all above info.) ....

....

Date new treats were introduced (and all above info.) ....

....

Date new table foods were introduced (and all above info.) ....

....

Foods or treats used to deliver medications: ....

....

Dietary supplements (here or on medication log in Section Eight): ....

....

Dental chews or treats: ....

Water additives or broths: ....

4
Cognitive health assessment

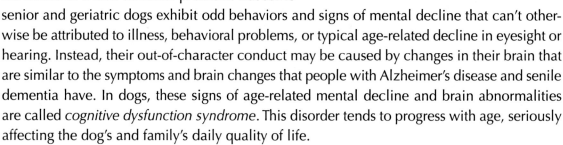

Changes in a dog's typical behavior or temperament at any age can signal illness or a new behavior problem. But some senior and geriatric dogs exhibit odd behaviors and signs of mental decline that can't otherwise be attributed to illness, behavioral problems, or typical age-related decline in eyesight or hearing. Instead, their out-of-character conduct may be caused by changes in their brain that are similar to the symptoms and brain changes that people with Alzheimer's disease and senile dementia have. In dogs, these signs of age-related mental decline and brain abnormalities are called *cognitive dysfunction syndrome*. This disorder tends to progress with age, seriously affecting the dog's and family's daily quality of life.

A dog's behavior changes may be subtle at first, and pet parents tend to attribute them to their dogs "just getting old" or "having senior moments." They can be as subtle as getting a little confused and turned around in the house, or as severe as anxious panting and pacing for hours on end. Although there is no cure for cognitive dysfunction in dogs, the sooner we catch it, the better chance we have to slow its progression. Recognizing the signs of cognitive dysfunction earlier in the course of the disease gives dogs and pet parents a better chance to effectively manage their dogs' signs and relish more happy, good-quality-of-life days together. Apparently healthy dogs can show signs of cognitive impairment as early as 6 years of age! Cognitive deficits tend to progress, but the rate of these changes varies—they may progress slowly or quickly.

Use the "Cognitive Assessment and Health Concerns for Dogs" checklist to monitor your dog, and go over it with your veterinarian if you notice changes. A diagnostic test isn't yet available to pinpoint cognitive dysfunction, so veterinarians must make a *diagnosis of exclusion*. This means we look first for another medical condition or behavioral problem that could be causing the pet's signs. Your veterinarian may ask you to complete a questionnaire or checklist designed to screen senior dogs for signs of cognitive dysfunction (similar to the checklist I provide here).

Complete this checklist and share it with your veterinarian during your dog's semi-annual examinations. Schedule a veterinary visit sooner anytime your dog's signs concern you, or if your dog exhibits any of these signs once a week or more.

Dog Cognitive
Assessment
Template

Cognitive Assessment and Health Concerns for Dogs

Date _____ Pet's Name _____ Age _____

Category	Sign	Does not occur or is not applicable	Occurs once a month	Occurs once a week	Occurs once a day/ night	Occurs more than once a day/night
DISORIENTATION	Appears lost/wanders between rooms without purpose					
	Paces back and forth excessively or circles					
	Vocalizes without apparent reason during the day or evening (barks or whines)					
	Vocalizes without apparent reason during sleeping hours (barks or whines)					
	Stares into space or stares absently at the floor or walls					
	Stands in corners					
	Gets stuck under or behind objects					
	Doesn't seem to recognize family members or housemate pets					
	Doesn't seem to recognize or is startled by familiar objects					
	Walks or bumps into doors or walls					
	Has trouble finding food that is dropped on the floor					
	Less interested in or less reactive to sights and sounds					
	Has trouble finding food or water bowl					
	Stands at the hinge side of the door to be let out					

Category	Sign	Does not occur or is not applicable	Occurs once a month	Occurs once a week	Occurs once a day/ night	Occurs more than once a day/night
	Appears lost in the yard or inappropriately wanders away from home					
	More reactive to sights and sounds					
	Increased fear of new places/locations					
INTERACTIONS	Disinterested in greeting family members					
	Hiding/sleeping in unusual places					
	Less interest in being petted					
	Irritable or aggressive with family members					
	Less interest in play with housemate pets					
	Irritable or aggressive with housemate pets					
	Increased anxiety when owners are away/doesn't like being left alone					
	More clingy					
	More aloof					
SLEEP/WAKE CYCLE	Awake less time during the day than asleep during the day					
	Agitated or restless during the day or evening					
	Awake at night more time than asleep at night					
	Paces at night					
	Agitated or restless during sleep hours					

Category	Sign	Does not occur or is not applicable	Occurs once a month	Occurs once a week	Occurs once a day/ night	Occurs more than once a day/night
HOUSE SOILING	Urinates inappropriately in the house					
	Defecates inappropriately in the house					
	Urinates inappropriately in front of owner					
	Defecates inappropriately in front of owner					
	Urinates but seems unaware					
	Defecates but seems unaware					
	Doesn't signal a need to go outside					
	Eliminates inappropriately indoors right after being outdoors					
	Urinates or defecates in unusual locations outdoors (on concrete)					
ACTIVITY AND LEARNING	Less or no interest in play or toys					
	Less or no interest in going for walks					
	Less or no interest in exploring					
	Seems to have forgotten trained commands or name					
	Difficulty learning new commands or routines					
	Decreased focus/hard to get and retain dog's attention					
	Exhibits repetitive behaviors					

Category	Sign	Does not occur or is not applicable	Occurs once a month	Occurs once a week	Occurs once a day/night	Occurs more than once a day/night
ADDITIONAL HEALTH CONCERNS	Vomiting					
	Diarrhea					
	Constipation					
	Straining to urinate					
	Straining to defecate					
	Vision loss					
	Hearing loss					
	Hair loss or thinning					
	Decreased appetite					
	Decreased water consumption					
	Increased appetite					
	Increased water consumption					
	Hesitant to jump up or down from favorite spots (couch, bed, car)					
	Hesitant or unwilling to use stairs					
	Limping					
	Weakness or lethargy					
	Seizures					

5

Symptom record

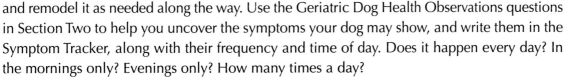

Tracking your dog's symptoms throughout their geriatric years helps you remember and realistically assess whether they have improved, stayed stable, or declined. This can help your veterinarian construct a veterinary care plan for your dog and remodel it as needed along the way. Use the Geriatric Dog Health Observations questions in Section Two to help you uncover the symptoms your dog may show, and write them in the Symptom Tracker, along with their frequency and time of day. Does it happen every day? In the mornings only? Evenings only? How many times a day?

Next note any circumstance that seems to be associated with the symptom, if applicable. For example, does vomiting, diarrhea, or disorientation occur only after your dog eats fatty snacks? Does your dog limp or have difficulty getting up from lying down only after walking up a flight of stairs? Does she have trouble recognizing family members or bump into furniture when the lights are low? Does he tire easily or cough only when playing with a furry sibling?

Symptom severity is the next aspect to document. Is it mild and your dog doesn't seem too bothered by it, or does it affect her for the rest of the day? You can also note whether it is a mild, moderate, or severe issue for you as the caregiver.

Finally, note improvements—what helps alleviate the symptom? Does your dog stop limping or wobble less when he finds better traction on the floor? Does your dog sleep through the night when you play soothing music or nature sounds, or when you sleep in the same room with him? Does he eat more when you soften or warm his food? Has a new medication helped?

Date each entry to help you monitor your dog. You'll see trends starting sooner rather than later and can make adjustments faster.

When tracking your geriatric dog's symptoms, keep in mind that with the exception of some conditions that may be treatable and resolve, you are not necessarily looking for perfection or a return to normal. You're looking for ways to help slow the progression of your dog's symptoms and help them live well by alleviating as much discomfort as possible—to provide care and love to the best of your abilities. All to help your dog feel better and have a good life quality—and help yourself do so as well.

Dog Symptom
Tracker

Symptom tracker

Pet's Name ....

Symptom	Date	Frequency and Time of Day	Association	Severity	Improvements

6

Veterinary visits and procedures

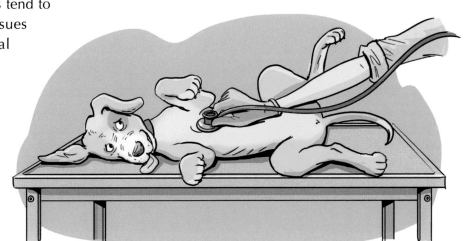

Like us as we age, dogs tend to have more health issues and need more medical attention during their last life stage. When dogs reach their senior and geriatric years, routine veterinary checkups are needed every six months. Why so many? Checkups help detect conditions and diseases associated with aging. Looking for and addressing health threats in your furry family members can help them live longer and more comfortably, all while allowing them to stay as active and engaged (and as happy) as possible. And like us, dogs who have chronic medical conditions usually need to see a veterinarian even more often than every six months for rechecks. A dog's final years are the most delicate, and your veterinary team can help shore up the precious time you have left with your dog.

Veterinary Visits and Procedures logs

Veterinary Visits and Procedures logs

Visit date .... Veterinary hospital ....

Veterinarian's name ....

Dog's Weight .... Body Condition Score .... Muscle Condition Score ....

Vaccinations .... Toenail trim ....

Diagnostic tests done (see also Section Seven) ....

....

....

....

Parasite Preventives Flea/Tick/Heartworm, other medications, supplements, diets, or other treatments prescribed (see also Section Eight) ....

....

....

....

....

....

....

....

Visit Summary/diagnosis/procedure ....

....

....

....

....

....

....

Next visit scheduled ....

7

Diagnostic tests

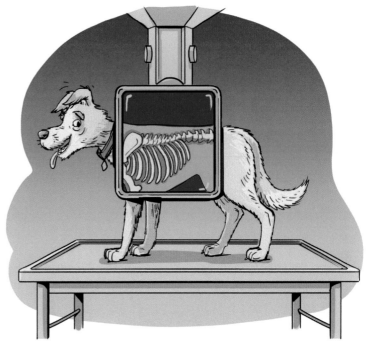

I recommend that senior and geriatric dogs have routine blood tests (complete blood count, serum chemistry profile), and a urine test (urinalysis) done every 6 to 12 months. In addition, your dog should have a heartworm test and fecal examination done yearly.

Your dog may have a condition that also requires additional types of blood tests (such as tests for infectious diseases or hormone imbalances), other diagnostic tests (such as x-rays, ultrasound, electrocardiogram, blood pressure measurement), or frequent rechecks of a specific blood test. Use the Diagnostic Test Tracker to monitor your dog's tests and record a summary of the results.

Glucose Trackers: For pet parents of dogs with diabetes, I've also included a form to monitor glucose and other parameters. Later there is an insulin tracker as well.

Dog Diagnostic
Test Tracker

Dog Glucose
Tracker

Diagnostic Test Tracker

Diagnostic Test Tracker

Pet's Name ....

Date	Test	Result Summary

Glucose Tracker

Pet's Name

Date	Blood Glucose Concentration	Urine Glucose	Urine Ketones	Notes (Attitude, Water consumption, Urination, etc)

8

Tracking treatments

Keeping good notes about your dog's medications, other therapies, and schedule changes is as important as tracking their symptoms. It becomes a handy reference for treatments you've tried or changes you've made and their effects.

Log each drug name, dose, frequency (how many times a day it's given) and duration (how long it's to be given), what it's used to treat or manage, and the result (whether it helped or if you noted side effects or new symptoms). If you adjust a dose or the number of times it's given, note that as well (note: all prescription medicine adjustments should be made according to your veterinarian's advice).

Remember to include medications, supplements, or nutraceuticals that you purchase over-the-counter. Also note any other therapy such as acupuncture, surgery, massage, chemotherapy, grooming, and any major schedule change such as boarding or daycare.

Remembering whether you gave your dog a medication can be difficult, especially if your dog receives more than one medication, has to take medications more often than twice a day, or if more than one person gives the medication. For example, my dog had to receive one medication to be given in the morning and in the evening on an empty stomach, another medication given three times a day with food, another medication given in the middle of the day, and another medication given before bed—for a whopping total of seven different times a day! I used a large multi-dose vitamin/pill container that I found online, and it made her pill times so much easier to manage.

Here I've provided a general treatment tracker, a medication log to track once or twice a day administration, and a log for therapies given more than twice a day and an insulin tracker for those administering insulin.

Treatments

Dog Medication Log (2 x)

Dog Medication Log (multiple)

Dog Insulin Tracker

Treatment tracker

Pet's Name ....

Date	Medication (and other therapy) or change in schedule	Dose	Frequency and Duration	What it's for	Result

Medication Administration Log (once or twice a day)

Pet's Name ....

Date	Medication	AM	PM

Medication Administration Log (more than twice a day)

Pet's Name

Date	Medication	Time 1	Time 2	Time 3	Time 4	Time 5	Time 6

Insulin Tracker

Pet's Name ....

Date	Feeding Time Morning	Insulin Dose and Time / Morning	Feeding Time Evening	Insulin Dose and Time / Evening

9

Counting breaths

If your dog has a respiratory condition or heart disease, then keeping tabs on their breathing rate and effort is especially important. The Respiratory Rate Tracker is perfect for that! While your dog is resting or sleeping, count how often they take a breath in 20 seconds and multiply that by three to determine their respiratory rate per minute. Your dog's ideal resting respiratory rate may depend on what medical condition your dog has and which medications your dog receives, so your veterinarian will advise you on the appropriate breaths per minute range. However, in general, if your dog's breathing rate is consistently over 30 breaths per minute while he is relaxed and resting or sleeping, call your veterinarian to schedule an evaluation.

Dog Respiratory
Rate Tracker

Respiratory Rate Tracker

Respiratory Rate Tracker

Count the number of breaths your dog takes in 20 seconds and multiply it by three to calculate the number of breaths per minute.

Pet's Name ....

My pet's resting respiratory rate/minute should be (according to my vet): ....

Date	Notes about the day/how my pet was breathing	Resting Rate/Minute AM	Resting Rate/Minute PM

10
Goals of care

My good friend and human hospice and palliative medicine physician BJ Miller co-wrote the book *A Beginner's Guide to the End: Practical Advice for Living Life and Facing Death*. It's a valuable reference for anyone facing a friend's, family member's, or their own end of life. I've refined a few tools I've been using over the years in my veterinary hospice practice based on some wonderful concepts from BJ's book. Based on the care goals exercise that BJ Miller outlines in his book, I advise pet parents to create a "Goals of Care" journal entry as well.

Thinking about your goals of care for your dog encourages you to collect your thoughts about the influences on your dog's and your experiences near the end of your dog's life. Writing down these goals helps you realistically assess the circumstances you're facing with regard to your dog's ailments and how much treatment you're willing to pursue. It helps you decide which goals and activities are most important for your dog and you, establish which compromises you're willing to make, and create a road map for how you'll meet your goals of care. This exercise also helps you consider whether your goals for your dog match up with your abilities to reach them.

Here are examples of care-oriented questions to ask yourself that will help you identify priorities as your pet experiences the limitations and illnesses that aging brings.

CIRCUMSTANCES: Write what you know about your dog's diagnosis or condition, and list the resources available to you.

Examples:

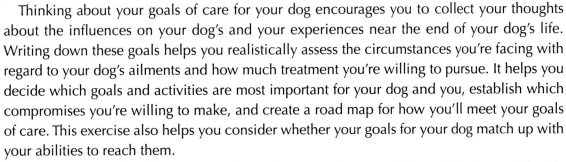

- Do you need family members and friends to help?
- Are they available and willing to help?
- Can you talk with your veterinarian regularly about your dog's care?
- As your dog's caregiver, what are your financial, physical, emotional, and time limitations?

Dog
Goals of Care

GOALS: Write what you want to do for your dog and for yourself as his caregiver.

Examples:

- Do you want your dog to receive all possible curative treatments?
- Or would you rather focus solely on relieving symptoms?
- Would you like to supplement your care with veterinary hospice care?
- Do you have a bucket list you'd like to fulfill for your dog?
- Do you want to plan for your dog to die at home rather than at the veterinary hospital?
- Do you want a veterinarian to end your dog's dying process before active suffering occurs?
- How would you like to memorialize your dog?

COMPROMISES: Truthfully draw your line in the sand. What trade-offs are you willing to make and not make?

Examples:

- Will you delay travel for months because your dog needs extensive care?
- Will you allow others to care for your dog if you need to be away?
- Is it acceptable to you that your dog may urinate on pee pads in their bed every night?
- Does it work with your schedule and finances to take your dog to physical rehabilitation or cancer therapy weekly?
- Are you OK with not trying or not providing certain therapies that may give you more time with your dog?
- Are you OK with not starting or with stopping certain therapies that are unlikely to help your dog?

ROAD MAP: List your next action items for providing care and meeting your goals within the guardrails of your compromises and limitations.

Examples:

- Do you need to put up baby gates or place bath mats across a slippery floor?
- Investigate veterinary physical rehabilitation therapy options?
- Arrange a trip to the beach to fulfill a bucket list item?
- Schedule a veterinary examination to provide comfort care or discuss hospice?
- Explore options for aftercare of your dog's body?

You may need to reexamine your goals of care every month as your dog's condition and your situation change. Your dog's care may be easy one month, but the next month you may feel overwhelmed in trying to control your dog's symptoms. I also suggest discussing your care goals with your veterinarian—this allows your veterinarian to understand your wishes and direct your dog's care appropriately.

GOALS OF CARE

Pet's Name .... Date ....

Circumstances	
Goals	
Compromises	
Road Map	

11

The adventures of a lifetime

I often suggest that pet parents create a bucket list of all the things they want to do for their dog or allow their dog to experience before they say their final goodbye. When you're thinking about the list, consider: What makes your dog your dog? What brings him pure joy? What brings her ordinary happiness? What 10 things do you want him to experience before you say goodbye?

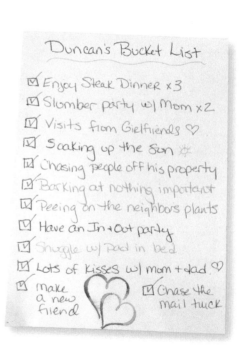

Add to the list or make different plans if your dog's health status changes. Start checking things off while you can both still relish the activities—whether it's weeks, months, or years before your dog earns angel wings.

Bucket list activities needn't be extravagant. I think it's safe to say most dogs, especially grey muzzles, savor the comforts of a stable routine and simple surprises. Two of the activities on my dog Duncan's bucket list were visits from all his girlfriends (the human ones, that is), plus a cheeseburger meal from In-N-Out Burger!

I love bucket lists because when it comes time to say goodbye to your dog, having checked off those special activities and experiences diminishes regret. It allows you to focus fully on the tender moments you have with your beloved dog in their final hours.

Dog
Bucket List

 My dog Duncan got to keep guard against strangers, the mail truck, and the neighbor's plants!

Duncan's Bucket List

☑ Enjoy Steak Dinner x3
☑ Slumber party w/ Mom x2
☑ Visits from Girlfriends ♡
☑ Soaking up the Sun ☀
☑ Chasing people off his property
☑ Barking at nothing important
☑ Peeing on the neighbors plants
☑ Have an In + Out party
☑ Snuggle w/ Dad in bed
☑ Lots of kisses w/ mom + dad ♡
☑ make a new friend   ☑ Chase the mail truck

............................'s

BUCKET LIST

- [ ] ....
- [ ] ....
- [ ] ....
- [ ] ....
- [ ] ....
- [ ] ....
- [ ] ....
- [ ] ....
- [ ] ....
- [ ] ....
- [ ] ....
- [ ] ....
- [ ] ....

12

Joyful living

One of my patient's families once wrote a "Favorite Things" list for their dog, and I like that twist. It may overlap with a Bucket List, but it's a bit different. For example, with my own dog Sam, I realized I needed both lists, for separate reasons. Sam's Bucket List contained the things I wanted her to be able to do before she passed, like take a trip to the river, enjoy a long car ride, and have an hour-long head scratching session. But when I wrote Sam's Favorite Things, I thought of the things that bring her joy all the time: her cherished stuffed animal that no one could touch, games of hide-and-go-seek, visits from my sister, and her favorite chewy toy.

Sam's Favorite Things helped me better assess her quality of life as her illness took its toll—were the things that brought her joy still bringing her joy? And when most of them didn't, that helped me better realize when it was time to say goodbye. I now encourage pet parents to create both lists, because they serve two different purposes.

Dog Joys of Living

 Henry's Favorite Things List

_____'s
FAVORITE THINGS

PHOTO

- [ ]
- [ ]
- [ ]
- [ ]
- [ ]
- [ ]
- [ ]
- [ ]
- [ ]
- [ ]
- [ ]
- [ ]
- [ ]

13

Assessing your dog's life quality

The most common question pet parents ask me is "How will I know when it's time to say goodbye?" This is not an easy answer, and during my conversation with pet parents, we discuss life quality considerations in four major categories: the pet's ailments and the expected progression of each ailment, the pet's personality, the pet parent's personal beliefs about when to say goodbye, and the pet parent's ability to care for their pet in terms of their own essential pet care budgets—financial, time, physical, and emotional. How a pet parent wishes to say goodbye—euthanasia or natural passing—is another consideration. A helpful way to evaluate your dog's life quality is with one of the many assessment tools available from a variety of sources. I've created one here. You may want to use one or more different assessment methods to consider your dog's physical, mental, and emotional well-being.

Dog Life
Quality Tool

Dog Life Quality Assessment

Write "1"' in the appropriate column to the right of the assessment parameter. At the bottom you'll tally the columns and calculate your dog's score.

Category	My Dog...	Often	Sometimes	No/Not Applicable
SLEEPING	Wakes once or more at night to go out to eliminate			
	Wakes once or more at night for no apparent reason, seems restless or anxious (pants, paces, whines)			
	Sleeps more than usual during the day			
	Sleeps less than usual during the night			
MENTATION	Wanders aimlessly around the house			
	Paces habitually in one location			
	Stares vacantly into space			
	Gets stuck or stands in corners or under furniture, or in unusual places in the yard			
	Seems anxious, restless or unsettled during waking hours			
	Is more clingy than normal			
	Wants to be left alone or seeks hiding spots			
	Shows less interest in exciting activities (riding in the car, greeting visitors, watching squirrels)			
	Seeks less attention (love and cuddles)			
	Shows less interest in playing with toys			
	Barks or whines for no apparent reason			
APPETITE AND THIRST	Has less interest in food or eats less than normal			
	Needs to be hand-fed			
	Refuses to eat			
	Seems nauseous or vomits one or more times a week			
	Drinks water more often			
	Requires subcutaneous fluid therapy			

Category	My Dog...	Often	Sometimes	No/Not Applicable
ELIMINATION	Has diarrhea or stool is soft and unformed			
	Has fecal incontinence one or more times a week			
	Urinates more than usual			
	Has urinary incontinence (dribbles urine after urinating normally or leaks urine while sleeping or resting)			
MOBILITY	Has difficulty lying down			
	Has difficulty getting up			
	Has difficulty walking up or down stairs or needs help			
	Drags a foot or toes when walking			
	Appears wobbly when walking			
	Takes shorter or less frequent walks than normal			
	Cannot run and play like before			
	Shows less interest in going for walks or normal play activities			
	Cannot jump up to or down from favorite spots like they used to			
APPEARANCE	Looks thinner or less muscular			
	Has a dull facial expression, is not bright and alert			
	Hangs head and seems listless			
	Has a bad odor from skin, ears, or mouth			
	Appears unkempt, has a rough, matted or thin haircoat or hair loss			
	Has pressure sores or scabs			
BREATHING	Pants more than normal			
	Tires easily with normal activity			
	Shows signs of difficulty breathing (anxious, wide-eyed expression when panting, increased chest expansion and abdominal push when inhaling, abnormal gum or tongue color)			
	Sounds different when barking (croaky, raspy or harsh)			
	Requires oxygen support			

Category	My Dog...	Often	Sometimes	No/Not Applicable
VISION	Has decreased vision			
	Bumps into objects, has difficulty finding bowls			
HEARING	Has decreased hearing			
	Startles easily when touched or seems less aware of approaching family members or other pets in the household			
PAIN OR DISCOMFORT	Is irritable or aggressive (growls, snaps or bites at people or other pets)			
	Resists being petted			
	Resists being picked up			

Total Assessment Factors	
Enter the total from the 'Often' column	
Halve the total from the Sometimes column. For example, if you answered "Sometimes'" 7 times, then enter 3.5.	
Add the value from the 'Often' column and the one-half value from the 'Sometimes' column. This is the total negative life quality score.	

Score interpretation	# of 'Negative Points'
Consider seeing your veterinarian to discuss the life quality factors you've marked.	Up to 8 points
Life quality is a concern, and your veterinarian can provide guidance on how to treat or help manage your dog's symptoms.	9–18 points
Life quality is deteriorating, and your dog would benefit from veterinary medical intervention to provide palliative care.	19–26 points
Life quality is poor. Consider veterinary hospice care or end-of-life discussions for your dog with your veterinarian.	27–36 points
Life quality is extremely poor. Consider euthanasia or palliative supported natural passing.	Over 36 points

14

Caring for caregivers

Caring for an ailing dog isn't easy. It can tax your relationships with family members, friends, and your dog. It can strain your emotions, physical ability, finances, and work and leisure schedules. Managing a dog's intense needs may negatively impact your quality of life. Throughout my career, I've helped countless families navigate the complexities of caring for their chronically ailing or terminally ill pets. And I've taken on the role of intense caregiver for many of my own dogs. I've mostly experienced enthusiasm, pride, joy, and contentment as a caregiver. And even though I love to do it, it's still a hard job. At times I've also been a tired, frustrated, mad, and stressed caregiver.

The number one reason why pet parents elect euthanasia for their dog is their dog's decreased quality of life. The number two reason is caregiver burden. If you're unable to take care of yourself, you'll be unable to care for others. I've created a chart to help you identify and reflect on some of the challenges and stressful feelings you may experience as you care for your ailing dog. My intention is not to determine whether you've had enough or whether you can handle more, because that is your personal decision. My intention is to help you remember you aren't alone in having these feelings. My hope is that in recognizing these challenges and feelings, you'll share them with your family, friends, and veterinary team to identify whether and what types of additional support may be available.

Dog Caregiver
QOL

50

Caregiver Assessment Chart(s)

Category	I...	Often	Sometimes	No, or not applicable to me or my family
SLEEPING	Wake up one or more times a night to take my dog out to eliminate or clean up an accident			
	Wake up one or more times a night to comfort my dog			
MENTATION	Worry about my dog when I am not home			
	Have to frequently monitor my dog's activities or whereabouts			
	Find my dog's confusion or disorientation difficult to manage			
	Am worried my dog is suffering			
	Am unsure how to evaluate my dog's happiness			
APPETITE, THIRST, MEDICATIONS, OTHER THERAPY	Have a hard time getting my dog to eat			
	Spend extra time preparing my dog's food			
	Am worried my dog is not eating enough			
	Am worried my dog is not drinking enough water			
	Struggle to give my dog medications			
	Have a hard time giving my dog subcutaneous fluids			
	Have a hard time giving my dog oxygen therapy			
	Have a hard time giving my dog physical therapy			
CLEANLINESS AND APPEARANCE	Often have to clean up my dog's urine or fecal accidents			
	Have a hard time keeping my dog clean			
	Often have to clean up my dog's vomit			
	Have to restrict my dog to a certain area or limit access to my home			
	Have a hard time keeping my dog's resting or sleeping areas clean			
	Am worried that my dog looks sick			
	Have a hard time brushing or bathing my dog			
	Cannot handle the way my dog smells			
	Am embarrassed to have visitors because of my dog's appearance, odor, or behavior			

Category	I...	Often	Sometimes	No, or not applicable to me or my family
MOBILITY	Have a hard time helping my dog get up			
	Have a hard time helping my dog use stairs			
	Cannot get my dog into or out of the car easily			
	Am unable to run or walk with my dog because of my dog's limitations			
	Am unable to play with my dog because of my dog's limitations			
HOUSEHOLD	Hear from others in my household who are angry with the dog			
	Have arguments about my dog's care with family or friends			
	Have to hide or quickly clean up my dog's accidents so others don't see them			
	Am irritated by my dog's loud panting			
	Have to warn or protect other pets, family members or friends because my dog may bite them			
	Have a hard time making physical adjustments in the household to meet my dog's mobility or comfort needs			
	Have a hard time making schedule adjustments in the household to meet my dog's needs			
CAREGIVING	Am stressed with the amount of care my dog needs			
	Feel overwhelmed by the amount of care my dog needs			
	No longer wish be my dog's caregiver			
	Would like or need more emotional support from others in providing care for my dog			
	Would like or need more physical help from others in providing care for my dog			
	Am struggling with anticipatory grief (feel overly anxious or depressed about the time I have left with my dog)			
	Feel anger toward my dog			
	Feel guilt about my dog's condition			
	Am worried I will allow my dog to suffer			
	Need help determining when is time to say goodbye to my dog			

Category	I...	Often	Sometimes	No, or not applicable to me or my family
BUDGETS	Cannot financially care properly for my dog			
	Cannot physically care properly for my dog			
	Cannot take the amount of time needed to properly care for my dog			
	Cannot emotionally care properly for my dog			

Total Assessment Factors	
Enter the total from the 'Often" column	
Halve the total from the Sometimes column. For example, if you answered "Sometimes'" 7 times, then enter 3.5.	
Add the value from the 'Often' column and the one-half value from the 'Sometimes' column. This is the total negative life quality score.	

The strain of caring for your pet is highly subjective. What one person can handle and what another can manage can be compeltely different. There is no 'wrong' way to feel. I believe it is good to ask yourself all of the qeustions above to honestly assess the different stressors you are dealing with—and maybe seek help with caregiving to help lighten the burden.

Below was my personal scoring system when managing my own dog's terminal illness. It may be helpful to you.

Caregiver Assessment	# of 'Negative Points'
You're managing your pet's ailments well. Consider talking with your veterinarian for additional suggestions that may make your pet's ailments easier to manage.	up to 10 points
The strain of caring for your pet may be negatively affecting your life quality. Make sure your pet is receiving medical attention so that ailments are managed appropriately. Look into ways to get help and take care of yourself.	11 - 20 points
Caring for your dog is negatively affecting your life quality. Remember, it's OK to be frustrated, sad, angry, confused, and a myriad of other emotions. It's also OK to consider end-of-life decisions for your dog, because their life quality is probably also quite diminished.	21 - 30 points
The burden you are feeling is considerable. Your dog's quality of life may also be poor. Consider end of life or palliative supported natural passing for your dog.	over 30 points

15

Dog days

Pet parents commonly tell me, "When my dog has more bad days than good days, then I will know it's time to say goodbye." In this case, it's important to measure what you're monitoring, because it can be difficult to accurately determine, "Is my dog having more bad days than good days?"

Using a simple tracking system such as a calendar helps. First write down what makes up a good day for your dog and you. This is different for everyone and every dog. Is sleeping eight hours straight good, or are you happy with four hours? Is a walk around the block good, or simply a stroll in the yard acceptable? Does a good day mean no accidents in the house, or is an occasional mess OK? Everyone in your household should agree on the definition of a good day. Then monitor your dog each day using those criteria to decide whether it's been a good day or a bad day.

If you use a calendar for making an end-of-life decision for your dog, you'll also want to determine what percentage of bad days is required before making that decision. Is it 50/50, or do you want your dog to enjoy good days 70% of the time? Or are good days 30% of the time still acceptable? Once you have decided on those parameters, then begin marking the bad days on a calendar. I suggest placing the calendar (you can copy or print out the template I provide here) somewhere easily visible, such as on your refrigerator. Simply write an 'X' or a sad face on a bad day, or write brief notes that describe the good and bad about the day.

Calendar
Template

QUALITY OF LIFE CALENDAR

MONTH

M	T	W	T	F	S	S

YOUR PET'S QUALITY OF LIFE SCORE $=\dfrac{\text{GOOD DAYS} \quad \square}{\text{BAD DAYS} \quad \square}$

NOTES

_____

_____

_____

2	Good quality of life
1.1-2	More good days than bad days but monitor quality of life
1	Good days = bad days
.5-.9	Bad days outnumber good days
.1-.4	Quality of life is not well. Discuss with a veterinarian.
0	No good days at all. Palliative sedation or euthanasia are warranted.

🐾 Dr Mary   www.drmarygardner.com